A Hunting I Will Go...

by

Tony Frizzell

DORRANCE
PUBLISHING CO
EST. 1920
PITTSBURGH, PENNSYLVANIA 15238

Dorrance Publishing Co
585 Alpha Drive
Suite 103
Pittsburgh, PA 15238
Visit our website at www.dorrancebookstore.com

ISBN: 978-1-6491-3459-2
eISBN: 978-1-6491-3812-5

A Hunting I Will Go...

When I grow up

I will get to hunt, too!

Just like my dad gets to do.

We will get up early

and pack our lunch,

grab our gear and head to the woods

to hunt a bunch.

Dad and I will hunt all day.

I hope Mr. Buck will come our way.

While in the woods we will

watch the birds and squirrels play

as they gather food for their long winter stay.

We will see the changing colors of the leaves
as they get ready to fall from the trees.

We will listen to the sounds

of the geese and ducks,

which will help pass the time,

as we wait for Mr. Buck.

We will sit in the stand, quiet and still,

hoping for the shot that will give us a thrill!

Dad says, "If we have good luck,

we will get to carry Mr. Buck home

in the back of the truck."

But, if luck is not on our side,

we will still be happy because we tried.

We will get to spend time together in the woods
and make lasting memories, as we should.

I will cherish these memories as I grow old,

and one day my kids will hear them told.

Hunting will be fun with my dad when I get to go

because I love spending time with him so.

OH!! I cannot wait until...

A Hunting I will Go!!!